E♭ Alto Saxophone Book 1

Tradition of Excellence™ Comprehensive Band Method

by Bruce Pearson & Ryan Nowlin

Dear Student:

Welcome to your study of the alto saxophone—an exciting adventure filled with rewards and challenges. Through careful study and regular practice, you will quickly discover the joy and satisfaction of playing beautiful music for yourself, your family, your friends, or a concert audience.

We wish you many rewarding years of alto saxophone playing.

Bruce Pearson

Ryan Nowlin

 *Interactive Practice*—the key to EXCELLENCE!

Make your practice sessions as fulfilling and productive as possible by frequently visiting your *Interactive Practice Studio* at www.kjos.com/ips.

 Hear each piece and play along! You can even change the speed. All recorded accompaniments can also be played from the DVD.

 Create recordings of your playing that you can save and email to friends, family, and your teacher.

 Learn to play your first notes, care for your alto saxophone, and overcome challenges as you progress. Alto saxophone video lessons feature Matt Best and can also be viewed from the DVD.

 Keep an eye out for fun Extras: stories behind the songs, classical and world music recordings, practice tips, a practice journal, and more!

 Use the Music Writer Touch software to complete written exercises and compose your own music.

 Download audio and video files to your computer and use them on your portable media device.

 Access your saved recordings for playback and sharing.

 Use the Tuner/Metronome during every practice session to improve your pitch and rhythm.

 *Tradition of Excellence* is available in SmartMusic. To subscribe go to www.smartmusic.com.

ISBN 10: 0-8497-7057-2 • ISBN 13: 978-0-8497-7057-9

 Tradition of Excellence and are trademarks of Kjos Music Press.

GETTING STARTED

For more detailed instruction, be sure to view the Video Lessons in your ***Tradition of Excellence Interactive Practice Studio*** or on the DVD. More lessons are available every time you see this icon.

Assembly

MOUTHPIECE

cork

reed

ligature

NECK

neck screw

BODY

1) Put the thin end of the reed in your mouth to moisten it. Grease the cork if necessary.

2) Gently twist the mouthpiece onto the neck. Properly align the flat side of the mouthpiece. ▶

3) Put the ligature on the mouthpiece. Loosen the ligature screws, slide it up slightly, and slip the reed behind it. Slide the ligature down.

4) Center the reed on the flat part of the mouthpiece with a hairline of mouthpiece visible above the reed. Tighten the screws on the ligature only until snug. ◀

5) Put the neck strap around your neck. Hook the neck strap to the body of the alto saxophone. ▶

6) Put the neck into the upper end of the body. Tighten the neck screw. ◀

Posture & Hand Position

1) Sit up straight at the edge and on the right side of your chair with your feet flat on the floor.
2) Place your right thumb under the lower thumb rest. Keep your thumb straight. Place your left thumb on the upper thumb rest at a 45-degree angle.

3) Position the alto saxophone on the right side of your body.
4) Adjust the mouthpiece, neck, and neck strap so that your head is straight.
5) Curve your fingers on both hands to form a relaxed "C," as if holding a tennis ball. Keep your wrists straight.
6) Relax your body. Keep your chin parallel to the floor and your elbows away from your body.

Forming an Embouchure & Making a Tone

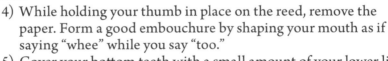

1) Remove the neck and mouthpiece from the body.
2) Slip a piece of paper between the reed and the mouthpiece, sliding it down away from the tip until it stops.
3) Put the tip of your thumb just under the imaginary line created by the paper. This line shows where your lower lip should be placed.
4) While holding your thumb in place on the reed, remove the paper. Form a good embouchure by shaping your mouth as if saying "whee" while you say "too."
5) Cover your bottom teeth with a small amount of your lower lip.
6) Place the mouthpiece in your mouth so your lower lip bumps against your thumb. Rest your top teeth directly on the mouthpiece. Close your lips like a drawstring. Your chin should be flat and pointed. Use a mirror to check your embouchure.
7) Take a full breath of air through your mouth and play a long, steady G♯.
8) Complete the **Mouthpiece Workout** by watching the video lesson and playing along with the recorded accompaniment (see page 1 for details).

Daily Care & Maintenance

1) Remove the ligature and reed. Place the reed in a reed holder to dry. Never store it on the mouthpiece.
2) Remove the mouthpiece and wipe the inside with a soft, clean cloth. Put the ligature back on and replace the cap.
3) Remove the neck, shake it and use the wool end of the neck cleaner to remove any moisture.
4) Dry the inside of the body by dropping a weighted swab into the top end and pulling the swab through.
5) Each time you finish caring for a part of the alto saxophone, return it to its proper place in the case. Latch the case.

ALTO SAXOPHONE LESSON

Terms & Symbols

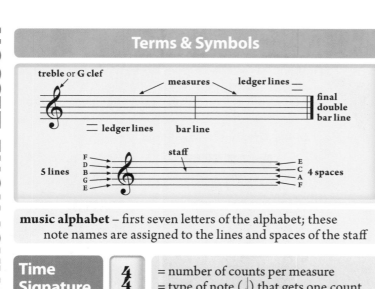

treble or G clef

measures

ledger lines

final double bar line

ledger lines

bar line

staff

5 lines

F
D
B
G
E

E
C
A
F

4 spaces

music alphabet – first seven letters of the alphabet; these note names are assigned to the lines and spaces of the staff

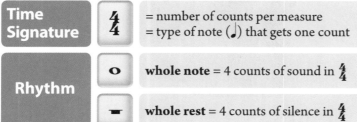

Time Signature 4/4

= number of counts per measure
= type of note (♩) that gets one count

Rhythm

o — **whole note** = 4 counts of sound in 4/4

— **whole rest** = 4 counts of silence in 4/4

Notes

○ = open   ● = pressed down

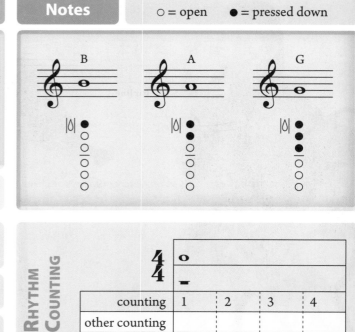

RHYTHM COUNTING

4/4	o			
	—			
counting	1	2	3	4
other counting				

To enhance practicing, use the recorded accompaniments, video lessons, and more provided in your *Tradition of Excellence Interactive Practice Studio*. See page 1 for more information.

staff & bar lines

4/4 o —

1. Busy "B"   ▸ How is your posture?

2. The "A" Train   ▸ Are you using plenty of air?

3. Music in Motion   ▸ Are you playing with a good embouchure?

4. "G" Whiz   ▸ How is your hand position?

5. Mr. Whole Note Takes a Walk   ▸ Write the note names beneath the music before you play.

WOODWIND LESSON

Terms & Symbols

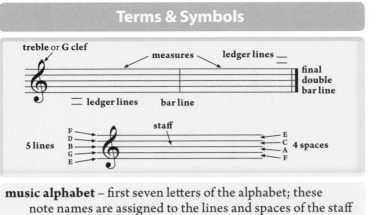

treble or G clef — measures — ledger lines — final double bar line

ledger lines — bar line

staff

5 lines — 4 spaces

music alphabet – first seven letters of the alphabet; these note names are assigned to the lines and spaces of the staff

Time Signature	$\frac{4}{4}$	= number of counts per measure = type of note (♩) that gets one count
Rhythm	o	**whole note** = 4 counts of sound in $\frac{4}{4}$
	▬	**whole rest** = 4 counts of silence in $\frac{4}{4}$

Notes

○ = open   ● = pressed down

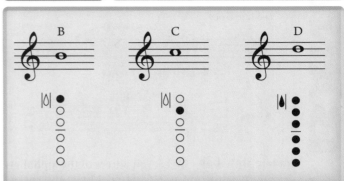

B   C   D

RHYTHM COUNTING

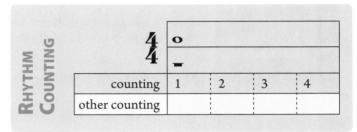

counting	1	2	3	4
other counting				

To enhance practicing, use the recorded accompaniments, video lessons, and more provided in your *Tradition of Excellence Interactive Practice Studio*. See page 1 for more information.

1. Woodwinds Unite   ▸ How is your posture?

2. Stepping Up   ▸ Are you using plenty of air?

3. Up 'n' Down 'n' Up   ▸ Are you playing with a good embouchure?

B   C   B   C

4. Up We Go   ▸ How is your hand position?

5. All Together, Now!   ▸ Write the note names beneath the music before you play.

D   C   B   D

FULL BAND

Terms & Symbols

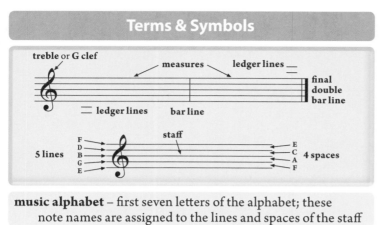

music alphabet – first seven letters of the alphabet; these note names are assigned to the lines and spaces of the staff

Time Signature	4/4	= number of counts per measure = type of note (♩) that gets one count
Rhythm	o	**whole note** = 4 counts of sound in 4/4
	▬	**whole rest** = 4 counts of silence in 4/4

Notes

○ = open ● = pressed down

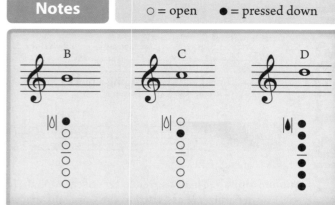

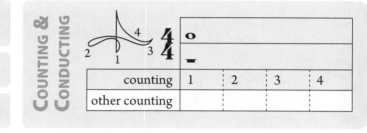

COUNTING & CONDUCTING

counting	1	2	3	4
other counting				

To enhance practicing, use the recorded accompaniments, video lessons, and more provided in your *Tradition of Excellence Interactive Practice Studio*. See page 1 for more information.

staff & bar lines

1. Away We Go!

▶ How is your posture?

2. Going Up?

▶ Are you playing with a steady air stream to produce a smooth, even sound?

3. Count Me In

▶ 1) Write the counting under the music. 2) Clap the rhythm.
3) Sing the notes using "too," the note names, or solfège. 4) Play!

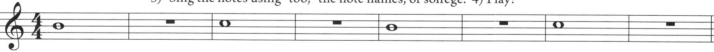

4. Higher Ground

▶ Are you playing with a good embouchure?

5. Moving Around

✓ TEST ▶ Write the note names beneath the music before you play.

6. Alto Saxophone Private Lesson

▶ Here is how to draw a treble clef. ▶ Draw eight treble clefs on your own. Be sure they circle the second (G) line.

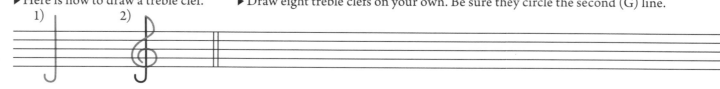

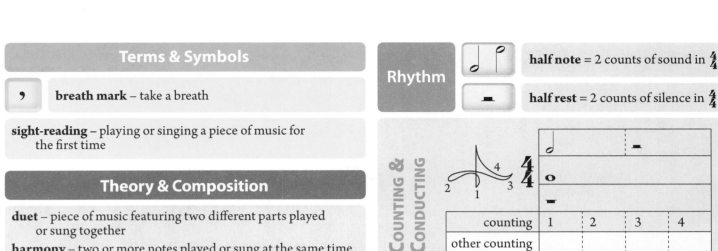

Terms & Symbols

,   **breath mark** – take a breath

sight-reading – playing or singing a piece of music for the first time

Theory & Composition

duet – piece of music featuring two different parts played or sung together

harmony – two or more notes played or sung at the same time

Rhythm

half note = 2 counts of sound in 4/4

half rest = 2 counts of silence in 4/4

COUNTING & CONDUCTING

counting	1	2	3	4
other counting				

7. Deep Breaths

rest = 4

8. Rhythm Time
▶ 1) Write the counting and clap the rhythm before you play. 2) Play on the note B (Concert D).

rest = 2

RHYTHM STUDIES: p. 44, #1-4

9. Half Note Rock

10. *Sight-Reading Challenge:* Steppin'
▶ Always carefully inspect music before you sight-read it.

11. El Camino Mariachi — *Duet*
▶ Count, clap, sing, and play! The B part is shaded for easier reading.

A.

B.

12. Cuckoo ✓ TEST

Traditional

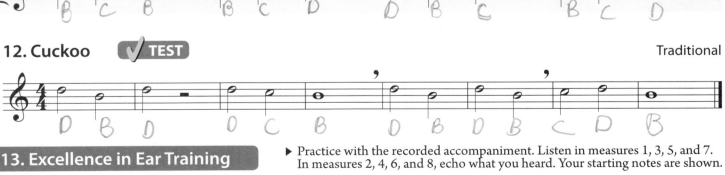

13. Excellence in Ear Training
▶ Practice with the recorded accompaniment. Listen in measures 1, 3, 5, and 7. In measures 2, 4, 6, and 8, echo what you heard. Your starting notes are shown.

1 Listen   2 Play   3 Listen   4 Play   5 Listen   6 Play   7 Listen   8 Play

W61XE

Rhythm

quarter note = 1 count of sound in $\frac{4}{4}$

quarter rest = 1 count of silence in $\frac{4}{4}$

COUNTING & CONDUCTING

	counting	1	2	3	4
	other counting				

Notes

A   G

14. Rhythm Time
▶ 1) Write the counting and clap the rhythm before you play. 2) Play on the note B (Concert D).

RHYTHM STUDIES: p. 44, #5-17

15. Rising Rhythms
▶ Start each note by whispering the word "too."

B B B B   B   C C C G   C   D D D D   D   B B B B   B

16. Stepping Stones
▶ Keep the air moving.

17. Rain, Rain
Traditional

18. In a Minor Mood
▶ Count, clap, sing, and play!

A

19. Hot Cross Buns
English Folk Song

G

B A   G   B A   G   G G G G   A A A A   B   A   G

20. Go Tell Aunt Rhodie   ✓ TEST
American Folk Song

21. Alto Saxophone Private Lesson
▶ 1) Draw a treble clef at the beginning of the staff.
2) Trace the notes and rests, and draw three more of each.

Terms & Symbols

Solo – only one person plays or sings
Soli – a small group or section plays or sings
Tutti – everyone plays or sings

repeat sign – play or sing the music again

Time Signature

C **common time** = $\frac{4}{4}$

Theory & Composition

phrase – musical sentence, often 4 or 8 measures long
round – song in which the same part is played or sung by two or more groups starting at different times
composition – creation of music that can be performed later, usually from written notation

22. Little Robin Redbreast
Traditional

23. Skill Builder: Merrily We Roll Along
▶ Count, clap, sing, and play! When you reach the end of the song, repeat once from the beginning.
Traditional

24. Itsy Bitsy Spider — *Round*
▶ Add brackets to show the phrases.
Traditional

25. A La Rueda
Spanish Folk Song

26. Love Somebody — *Duet*
Traditional

27. Good King Wenceslas   ✓ TEST
Traditional English Carol

C C C D   C C G   A G A B C   C   C C C D   C C G   A G A B   C   C

28. Excellence in Composition
▶ 1) Draw a treble clef. 2) Complete and play your composition.

Title _____   Composer _____

Terms & Symbols

articulation – type of attack used to play a note or group of notes

slur – articulation that connects notes of *different* pitches; indicates a very smooth sound with only the first note tongued

Notes

one-measure repeat sign – play or sing the previous measure again

29. Warm-up: Serenity — *Round*   ▶ Keep the air moving.

30. Chop Builder   ▶ Are you slurring?

C D   E D C   B E B E   B E B e C

31. Camptown Races   ▶ Draw the missing notes in the ovals before you play.

Stephen Foster, America's first great popular songwriter, was born on the 50th anniversary of American Independence: the Fourth of July, 1826.

Stephen Foster (1826–1864) American Composer

Solo/Soli   Tutti   Solo/Soli   Tutti

32. Skill Builder   ▶ Add brackets to show the phrases.

33. London Bridge — *Duet*   English Folk Song

A.

D E D C   B C D   A B C   D E D C   B C D   A D   B G

B.

34. The Frog's Song — *Round*   ✓ TEST   Japanese Folk Song

G A B C B A G   B C D E   D C B   G   G   G A B E   B A G

35. Alto Saxophone Private Lesson   ▶ Are you storing your reeds and swabbing your alto saxophone properly after each use?

MASTERING EXCELLENCE: p. 38, #1

Time Signature

$\frac{2}{4}$ = two counts per measure
= quarter note gets one count

COUNTING & CONDUCTING

	counting	1	2
	other counting		

Key Signature

sharp (♯) or flat (♭) signs placed after a clef

In these key signatures, play or sing:

no sharps or flats	every F as F sharp	every B as B flat	every B as B flat, every E as E flat

Rhythm

tie – marking that connects notes of the *same* pitch to make one longer note

Notes

F sharp (F♯)

Terms & Symbols

accidental – symbol that alters the pitch of a note until the end of the measure

♯ **sharp** – raises the pitch of a note one half step

F → F♯

Theory & Composition

interval – distance between two pitches
half step – smallest interval used in Western music; on a piano keyboard, it is the distance from one key to the very next key—white or black

$\frac{2}{4}$ **36. Rhythm Time** ▸ 1) Write the counting and clap the rhythm before you play. 2) Play on the note A (Concert C).

RHYTHM STUDIES: p. 44, #18-20; p. 46, #41-43

signature **37. Two Step** ▸ Circle the notes changed by the G major (Concert B♭ major) key signature, highlighted in purple.

dental, ♯

F♯

38. *Sight-Reading Challenge:* **Shoo Fly** American Folk Song

B G G A B C A   A F F G A B G

B G G A B C A   D D D C B A G

39. Russian Folk Song — *Duet*

Beethoven bridged music history's Classical and Romantic Periods.

Ludwig van Beethoven (1770–1827)
German Composer

A.

B.

40. San Serení ✓ **TEST** ▸ Add brackets to show the phrases. Puerto Rican Folk Song

41. Excellence in Theory ▸ Add the notes and rests together to find the number of counts. A quarter note gets one count.

a) ♩ + ♩ = ___   b) ♩ + 𝅗𝅥 = ___   c) 𝄽 + ♩ + − = ___   d) 𝅝 + − = ___

Theory & Composition		Terms & Symbols	
trio – piece of music featuring three different parts played or sung together			**rehearsal numbers** – find important places in the music using these markers
introduction – opening passage of a piece of music		1. 2.	**1st and 2nd endings** – play or sing the 1st ending the first time through, repeat, skip the 1st ending, and play or sing the 2nd ending the second time through
theme – a melody within a piece of music		𝄐	**fermata** – hold a note or rest longer than its usual value

Concert Etiquette —Enter the stage or performance area confidently. Make eye contact with the audience and smile.
—Stand or sit tall. Be positive and energetic. It's fun to share your music with others!

trio, introduction, theme

rehearsal numbers, 1st & 2nd endings

Solo: A   **Duet:** A + B   **Trio** or **Full Band:** A + B + C

Jingle Bells

J.S. Pierpont (1822–1893)
American Composer

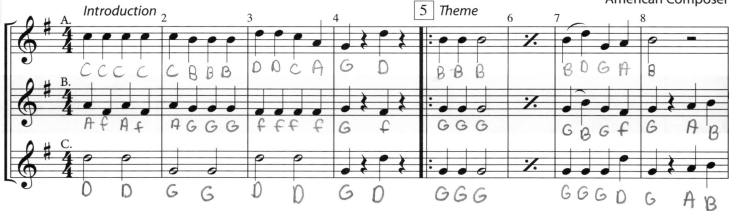

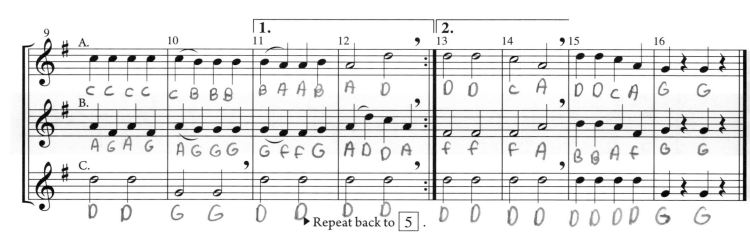

Jolly Old St. Nicholas

Traditional

The Dreidel Song

Jewish Folk Song

Kwanzaa Celebration

David Bobrowitz (b. 1945)
American Composer

14

Rhythm

eighth note = ½ count of sound in $\frac{2}{4}$, $\frac{4}{4}$, or **C**

a single eighth note has a **flag**

a group of eighth notes is connected by a **beam**

COUNTING & CONDUCTING

$\frac{4}{4}$ or **C**

	counting	1	&	2	&	3	&	4	&
	other counting								

42. Warm-up: Breath Support Challenge ▸ Take a deep breath and play with your best tone while holding the pitch for as long as you can. On which beat did you finish?

43. Epic Eighth Notes ▸ The bottom line provides the basic pulse.

44. Michael Finnegan ▸ Count, clap, sing, and play! Irish Folk Song

45. Eighth Note Escapade

46. Skill Builder: Processional Dance ▸ Count, clap, sing, and play! Renaissance Dance Music

47. Baja Breeze ✓ **TEST**

48. Alto Saxophone Private Lesson ▸ 1) Write the note names. 2) Fill in the fingering chart for each note.

W61XE

Theory & Composition

improvisation – spontaneous composition of music through playing or singing

49. Unforgettable Eighth Notes

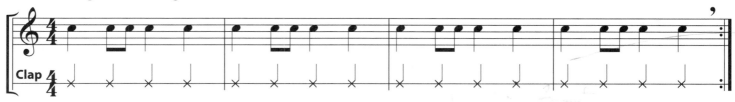

50. Mahnomen Harvest ▶ Count, clap, sing, and play!

A A C C D C A A C A G A A C A A G A A

51. Eighth Notes on the Edge

52. Now Let Me Fly ▶ Count, clap, sing, and play!

Spirituals are religious folk songs created in the 18th and 19th centuries.

American Spiritual

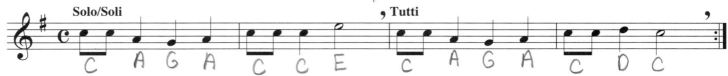

Solo/Soli   Tutti

C A G A C C E C A G A C D C

53. *Sight-Reading Challenge:* Promenade   ▶ 1) Write the counting and draw the bar lines. 2) Sight-read!

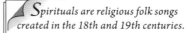

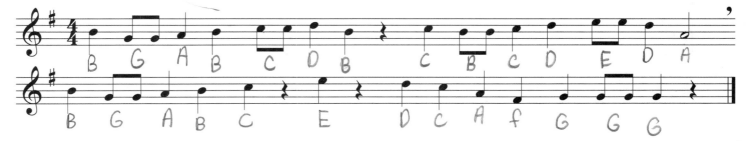

B G A B C D B C B C D E D A

B G A B C E D C A F G G G

54. Rio Con Brio   ✓ TEST

B B D B C D A A A C A B C D

B B D B C D E D B D C A F G

55. Excellence in Improvisation   ▶ Play along with the recorded accompaniment. Measures 1-2: Play the written notes. Measures 3-5: Improvise using the same notes.

1   2   3 Improvise – – – – – – 4 – – – – – – – – 5 – –

W61XE

Terms & Symbols

♮ **natural** – cancels a flat (♭) or sharp (♯)

♭ **flat** – lowers the pitch of a note one half step

Rhythm

pick-up or **anacrusis** – music that comes before the first full measure; rhythmic value of the pick-up is sometimes removed from the last measure

Notes

Key Signature

C major (Concert E♭ major) – indicates no sharps or flats

Theory & Composition

theme and variation – type of composition that begins with a main melody (**theme**) and continues with different versions (**variations**) of the main melody

56. Warm-up: Chorale — *Duet*

57. Rhythm Time
▶ 1) Write the counting and clap the rhythm before you play. 2) Play on the note C (Concert E♭).

RHYTHM STUDIES: p. 45, #21-35; p. 46, #44-46

58. Skill Builder: Boil the Cabbage Down — *Duet*
▶ Circle every F♮.   American Folk Song

59. Bingo Variations   ✓ TEST
▶ 1) Play the black notes, which make up the theme.
2) Add the gray notes, which make up the variation.   American Folk Song

60. Alto Saxophone Private Lesson

MASTERING EXCELLENCE: p. 38, #2

Rhythm · **dot** – adds half the value of the note

Time Signature **3/4** = three counts per measure = quarter note gets one count

Terms & Symbols

dynamics – softness or loudness of a piece of music

♩. = ♩ ♪ = ♩.
2 + 1 = 2 + 1 = 3

dotted half note = 3 counts of sound in 3/4, 4/4, or **C**

COUNTING & CONDUCTING

	counting	1 &	2 &	3 &
	other counting			

p **piano** – soft

f **forte** – loud

61. Rhythm Time

▶ 1) Write the counting and clap the rhythm before you play. 2) Play on the note C (Concert E♭).

RHYTHM STUDIES: p. 46, #49-53

62. Encounter in Three

▶ Circle every F♮.

63. Skill Builder: A Simple Waltz

64. *Sight-Reading Challenge:* Theme from "Cambridge Overture"

Anne McGinty is one of the most prolific female composers of band music and has over 225 pieces published for band, orchestra, and flute.

Anne McGinty (b. 1945) American Composer

1. **2.**

From *Cambridge Overture* (Q881077), ©1991 Edmondson & McGinty. All rights assigned Queenwood/Kjos 2002. Used with permission.

65. I've Just Come From Sydney ✓ TEST

Australian Folk Song

66. Excellence in Composition: Carnival of Venice

Italian Folk Song

▶ 1) Play the theme. 2) Add eighth notes after some of the quarter notes to compose a variation as in **59. Bingo Variations**. **Bonus:** Improvise a variation!

1. **2.**

Terms & Symbols	tempo – speed of a piece of music **Andante** – walking tempo; slower than **Moderato** **Moderato** – medium tempo **Allegro** – fast tempo	*mp*	*mezzo piano* – medium soft		accent – emphasize the note
		mf	*mezzo forte* – medium loud		

Andante

67. Warm-up: Lullaby
Welsh Folk Song

Andante

p

Allegro

68. Ezekiel Saw the Wheel — *Duet*
American Spiritual

Allegro

A.
p   *f*   *p*   *f*

B.
p   *f*   *p*   *f*

mp, >
Moderato

69. Rhythm Time
▶1) Write the counting and clap the rhythm before you play. 2) Play on the note G (Concert B♭).

mp

RHYTHM STUDIES: p. 46, #54-58

70. *Sight-Reading Challenge:* Streets of Laredo
Laredo is a city in Texas on the Mexican border.
American Folk Song

Moderato

mp

mf

71. Skill Builder: Donkey Riding
▶ 1) Add brackets to show the phrases.
2) Add a breath mark between the phrases.
Canadian Folk Song

Moderato

mf

72. Theme from "The Nutcracker" ✓ TEST
Tchaikovsky first studied to be a lawyer but eventually became a full-time composer thanks to the support of a wealthy patron.
Peter Ilyich Tchaikovsky (1840–1893)
Russian Composer

Andante

mp   *mf*

73. Alto Saxophone Private Lesson
▶Increase the tempo slightly each time you practice this exercise.
Learning these finger patterns is important to your progress.

MASTERING EXCELLENCE: p. 38, #3

Concert Etiquette

As a soloist, at the end of your performance, bow to acknowledge the applause of the audience, then gratefully gesture towards your accompanist so that he or she may also receive recognition from the audience.

SOLO

In addition to his work as a composer and author, Ryan Nowlin is a music teacher, horn player, and singer.

The Good Life
Solo with Piano Accompaniment

Ryan Nowlin (b. 1978)
American Composer

BAND PIECES

Theory & Composition	Terms & Symbols

chord – two or more notes sounded at the same time

closing – last measures of a composition, often containing music added to give a feeling of finality

long rest or **multiple-measure rest** – rest for the number of measures indicated

Concert Etiquette

—If you make a mistake, never let it show. Keep playing or singing as if nothing happened.

—When you are finished, graciously accept the audience's applause. Leave the stage area confidently.

chord

Warm-up: Tone, Balance, and Tuning

▶ There are many ways to perform a warm-up; follow the instructions given by your director.

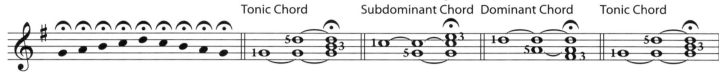

closing

long rest

Bruce Pearson played clarinet and saxophone as well as baseball and hockey into his college years before becoming a music teacher, author, composer, and conductor.

March Across the Seas

Bruce Pearson (b. 1942) and
Ryan Nowlin (b. 1978)
American Composers

Water Music was written for a royal boat party on England's Thames River. The orchestra played from one barge while King George I and friends listened from another vessel close by.

Procession
from "Water Music"

George Frideric Handel (1685–1759)
English Composer
arr. Ryan Nowlin

▶ In ²⁄₄, ³⁄₄, and other time signatures, ▬ indicates a full measure of rest.

Banana Boat Song

Jamaican Folk Song
arr. Ryan Nowlin

Indigo Rock

Bruce Pearson & Ryan Nowlin
American Composers

Terms & Symbols

crescendo – gradually louder
decrescendo – gradually softer

divisi (div.) – some performers play or sing the top notes while others play or sing the bottom notes

unisono (unis.) – everyone plays or sings the same notes

Notes

F   F sharp (F#)   E   D
alternate

74. Warm-up: "Werde munter" — *Duet*

*Johann Schop was a virtuoso violinist but also played cornet and trombone. This melody by Schop was used by J.S. Bach in his famous **Cantata 147**.*

Johann Schop (1590–1667)
German Composer

Andante

75. Fais Dodo

French Folk Song

Andante

76. Baroque March

Though considered an English composer, Handel was born in Germany.

George Frideric Handel (1685–1759)
English Composer

Moderato

divisi,
unisono

77. La Bamba

▶ Circle every F♮.

Mexican Folk Song

Allegro   div.   unis.

78. Skill Builder   ✓ TEST

Moderato

79. Alto Saxophone Private Lesson

▶ Use the alternate F# fingering on notes with ∗ .

A

B

E   D

MASTERING EXCELLENCE: p. 38, #4

Theory & Composition

whole step – interval consisting of two half steps

major scale – series of whole (w) and half (h) steps
in the following pattern: 1 2 3 4 5 6 7 8
⌣⌣⌣⌣⌣⌣⌣
w w h w w w h

arpeggio – notes of a chord sounded one after another

orchestration – choice of instruments used to play the music

Notes

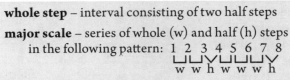

F sharp (F♯)   G

80. Going Up or Down?

81. Just By Accident

▶ Use the alternate F♯ fingering on notes with ✳.

82. *Sight-Reading Challenge:*
Theme from "Orpheus In the Underworld"

In addition to composing, Jacques Offenbach was a fine cellist.

Jacques Offenbach (1819–1880)
French Composer

83. G Major Scale, Arpeggio, and Chords (Concert B♭ Major)

84. Crescent Moon Rising

Chinese Folk Song

Orchestration: Full Band ———— Woodwinds & Percussion ———— Brass & Percussion ———— Full Band ————

85. Skill Builder ✓ TEST

▶ Also play with other articulations:

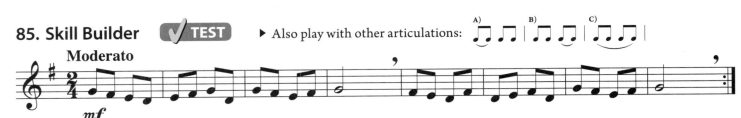

86. Excellence in Improvisation

▶ Play along with the recorded accompaniment. Measures 1-2: Play the written notes.

Measures 3-5: Improvise using [staff notation].

W61XE

Terms & Symbols	Key Signature	Notes
courtesy accidental or **cautionary accidental** – reminder that the bar line has canceled an accidental	**D major (Concert F major)** – play or sing every F as F♯, C as C♯	C sharp (C♯) F sharp (F♯) alternate

courtesy accidental

87. Warm-up: Chop Builders

88. Song of Remembrance

89. D Major Scale, Arpeggio, and Chords (Concert F Major)

90. Santa Lucia   ▶ Circle the notes changed by the key signature.   Italian Folk Song

91. *Sight-Reading Challenge:* Boogie Blues

92. Skill Builder ✔ TEST

93. Alto Saxophone Private Lesson   ▶ Use the alternate F♯ fingering on notes with ∗.

MASTERING EXCELLENCE: p. 38, #5

W61XE

Terms & Symbols

staccato – shorten the note

Notes

94. Warm-up: Tone Builder
Andante

95. C Major Scale, Arpeggio, and Chords (Concert E♭ Major)
Major Scale · Arpeggio · Chords *div.*

96. When the Saints Go Marching In
When the Saints Go Marching In is often performed in a Dixieland jazz style. Dixieland originated in New Orleans, Louisiana in the early 20th century.
American Spiritual
Allegro

97. Musette
Bach's death marked the end of the Baroque Period.
Johann Sebastian Bach (1685–1750)
German Composer
Allegro · Solo/Soli · Tutti

98. Bella Bimba
Italian Folk Song
Moderato

99. Skill Builder ✓ TEST
▶ Use the alternate F♯ fingering on notes with ∗.
Moderato

100. Excellence in Ear Training
▶ Practice with the recorded accompaniment. Listen in measures 1, 3, 5, and 7. In measures 2, 4, 6, and 8, echo what you heard. Your starting notes are shown.

1 Listen 2 Play 3 Listen 4 Play 5 Listen 6 Play 7 Listen 8 Play

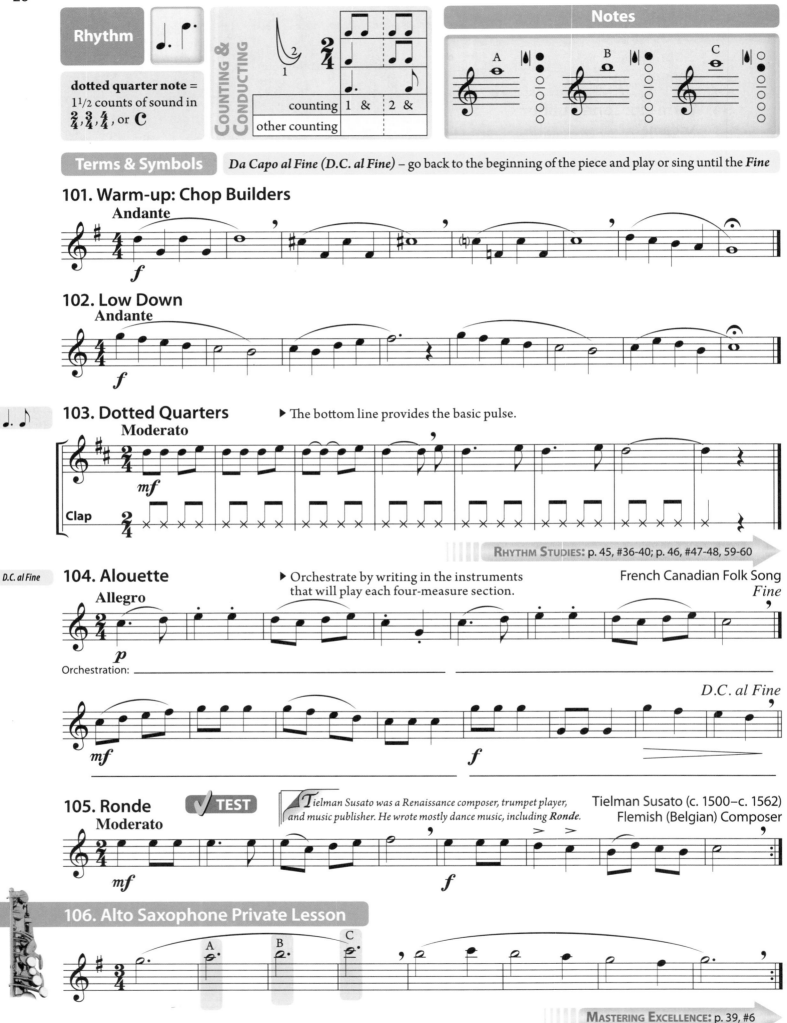

Rhythm ♩. ♪.

dotted quarter note = 1½ counts of sound in ²⁄₄, ³⁄₄, ⁴⁄₄, or **C**

COUNTING & CONDUCTING

counting	1	&	2	&
other counting				

Notes

Terms & Symbols — *Da Capo al Fine (D.C. al Fine)* – go back to the beginning of the piece and play or sing until the *Fine*

101. Warm-up: Chop Builders
Andante

102. Low Down
Andante

103. Dotted Quarters
♩. ♪
▶ The bottom line provides the basic pulse.
Moderato

Clap

RHYTHM STUDIES: p. 45, #36-40; p. 46, #47-48, 59-60

104. Alouette
D.C. al Fine
▶ Orchestrate by writing in the instruments that will play each four-measure section.
French Canadian Folk Song
Fine
Allegro

Orchestration: _____

D.C. al Fine

105. Ronde
✓ TEST
Tielman Susato was a Renaissance composer, trumpet player, and music publisher. He wrote mostly dance music, including Ronde.
Tielman Susato (c. 1500–c. 1562)
Flemish (Belgian) Composer
Moderato

106. Alto Saxophone Private Lesson

MASTERING EXCELLENCE: p. 39, #6

Terms & Symbols **Maestoso** – majestically

107. Soar!

Andante

mp ——— *f* *mp* ——— *f*

mp ——— *f* *mp* ——— *f*

108. Skill Builder

Moderato

1. **2.**

mf

109. *Sight-Reading Challenge:* Theme from "The Red Balloon"

Anne McGinty (b. 1945)
American Composer

Moderato

p

From *The Red Balloon* (Q882119), ©1993 Edmondson & McGinty. All rights assigned Queenwood/Kjos 2002. Used with permission.

aestoso

110. Trumpet Voluntary — *Duet* ✓ TEST

Trumpet Voluntary is also known as *Prince of Denmark's March* and was originally composed for harpsichord.

Jeremiah Clarke
(c. 1674–1707)
English Composer

Introduction
Maestoso

A.

f *Theme* *mf*

B.

f *mf*

A.

B.

1. **2.**

111. Excellence in Theory

▶ Add the notes and rests together to find the number of counts. A quarter note gets one count.

a) ♩ + ♩. = ___

b) ♩ + ‒ = ___

c) ♩. + ♩ + ♫ = ___

d) ‒ + ♪ + ♩. = ___

112. Warm-up: Range, Tone, and Tuning

Andante

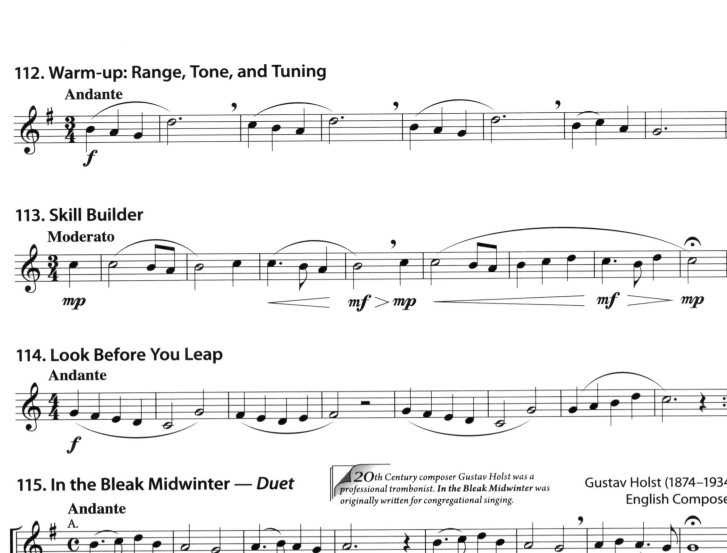

113. Skill Builder

Moderato

114. Look Before You Leap

Andante

115. In the Bleak Midwinter — *Duet*

> **20**th Century composer Gustav Holst was a professional trombonist. **In the Bleak Midwinter** was originally written for congregational singing.

Gustav Holst (1874–1934)
English Composer

Andante

A.

B.

116. Theme from "Symphony No. 9" ✓ **TEST**

> **B**eethoven was completely deaf when he wrote Symphony No. 9 in 1824.

Ludwig van Beethoven
(1770–1827)
German Composer

Moderato

117. Alto Saxophone Private Lesson

▶ 1) Write the note names. 2) Fill in the fingering chart for each note.

Erin Watson was born in Wichita Falls, Texas, the Lone Star State. She plays violin, piano, and accordion. She studied with famed American composer Joan Tower.

118. Lone Star Waltz

▶ 1) Orchestrate by writing in the instruments that will play each two-measure section of the music. 2) Add dynamics.

Erin A. Watson (b. 1977)
American Composer

Andante

119. *Sight-Reading Challenge:* Yangtze Boatman Chantey

▶ 1) Add brackets to show the phrases. 2) Add a breath mark between the phrases.   Chinese Folk Song

Andante

120. E–Z Does It

Andante

121. Mary Ann — *Duet*

Moderato

Calypso began in early 20th century Caribbean communities where slaves used music to communicate without their master's understanding. Today, the music often features guitar, steel drums, and other percussion instruments accompanying the vocals.

Calypso Song

122. Skill Builder: Happy Little Donkey — *Round*   ✓ TEST

Andante

American Folk Song

123. Excellence in Ear Training

▶ Practice with the recorded accompaniment. Listen in measures 1, 3, 5, and 7. In measures 2, 4, 6, and 8, echo what you heard. Your starting notes are shown.

1 Listen   2 Play   3 Listen   4 Play   5 Listen   6 Play   7 Listen   8 Play

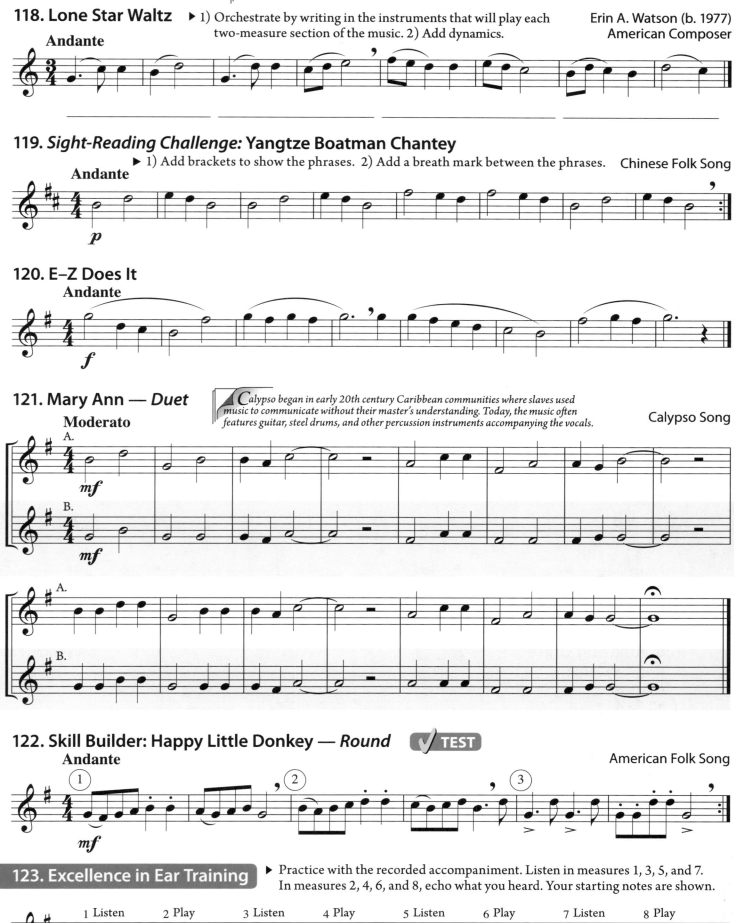

Terms & Symbols	Notes

ritardando (*ritard.* or *rit.*) – gradually slow the tempo

124. Warm-up: Chop Builders
Moderato

125. Oh Yeah!
Andante

126. Skill Builder
Andante

ritardando

127. Theme from "The Sleeping Beauty"
▶ Circle every F♮.

In 1891, Tchaikovsky traveled to America for the opening of Carnegie Hall in New York City.

Peter Ilyich Tchaikovsky
(1840–1893)
Russian Composer

Allegro

128. Amazing Grace   ✓ TEST
American Folk Song
Andante

129. Alto Saxophone Private Lesson
▶ Use the alternate C fingering when moving from B to C or C to B.

MASTERING EXCELLENCE: p. 39, #7

W61XE

31

| Rhythm | | **syncopation** – rhythmic effect that places emphasis on a weak beat |

130. A Little Blue

Moderato

The blues developed in the United States during the early 1900s as an outgrowth of African-American spirituals and work songs. Blues melodies are usually 12 measures long.

f
G D C D GG DD C D GDD C C D C E EGG E C E EGG E

G DD C D G d d f E D G G ED C D DD C C D f

131. Classical Dance

Mozart was a child prodigy, and he traveled throughout Europe with his father to display his talents on keyboard and violin. He composed his first symphony at age 8 and his first opera at age 12.

Wolfgang Amadeus Mozart
(1756–1791)
Austrian Composer

Allegro

f p rit.

132. Sound of Syncopation

▸ The bottom line provides the basic pulse.

Moderato

mf

Clap

133. Sleeping Princess

Swedish Folk Song

Moderato

mf
E D c a g B B a c C B D D E D c a g B B D D g f g
O D

134. Skill Builder: Samba-lêlê ✓ TEST

Brazilian Folk Song

Moderato

mf

135. Excellence in Theory

A. Write these tempo marks in the correct blanks: *slowest* ⟷ *fastest*

Andante Allegro Moderato _____ _____ _____

B. Write these dynamic marks in the correct blanks: *softest* ⟷ *loudest*

mf *p* *f* *mp* _____ _____ _____ _____

W61XE

136. Warm-up: Ye Banks and Braes o' Bonnie Doon — *Duet*

Scottish Folk Song

137. Open the Door for Me!

▶ Add brackets to show the phrases.

South African Folk Song

138. Shepherd's Hey

*Australian-born composer Percy Grainger (1882-1961) is well known for his arrangements of English folk songs and country dances. His 1918 version of **Shepherd's Hey** for concert band shows Grainger's skills in orchestration, and is part of the band world's standard repertoire.*

English Folk Song

139. The Yellow Rose of Texas

American Folk Song

140. Manhattan Beach March ✓ TEST

▶ Use the alternate F♯ fingering on the note with *.

Sousa played piano, violin, flute, cornet, trombone, and baritone. He is most remembered for his marches, and is known as "The March King."

John Philip Sousa
(1854–1932)
American Composer

Ensemble

*The term "military band" was historically used to designate an instrumental ensemble made up of woodwinds, brass, and percussion, much like today's concert band. Ecossaise for Military Band was originally written by Beethoven in 1810 for this type of ensemble. The work is a **contradance**, a lively dance-inspired composition in ²/₄. In a contradance, couples faced each other in two lines. It was a Classical Period predecessor to more modern forms such as square dancing.*

Solo: A **Duet:** A + B **Trio** or **Full Band:** A + B + C

Ecossaise for Military Band

▶ 1st x = first time through. 2nd x = second time through.

Ludwig van Beethoven (1770–1827)
German Composer
arr. Bruce Pearson

BAND PIECES

Theory & Composition

ternary form – music with three sections: Section A, followed by a contrasting Section B, then Section A again

trio – third theme in a march, typically a contrasting section

Concert Etiquette

Dress nicely for every performance. If no specific guidelines are given by your director, be sure to ask what is appropriate. When you look your best, the audience will more fully appreciate your playing or singing.

See, the Conquering Hero Comes
from "Judas Maccabaeus"

Judas Maccabaeus, composed in 1746, is one of Handel's most famous oratorios. This piece majestically commemorates the title character's victorious return from battle.

George Frideric Handel (1685–1759)
English Composer
arr. Ryan Nowlin

ternary form

Riverside March

Ryan Nowlin (b. 1978)
American Composer

▶ Notice the key signature changes at 27 and 47.

Minuet *is a general term for a triple meter dance that originated in France. It was popular in the 17th and 18th centuries and it was often included as a movement in sonatas, string quartets, and symphonies. Ignaz Pleyel was a pianist, composer, and a student of Haydn. He even started his own piano factory!*

▶ Notice the key signature changes at 21 and after measure 36.

Minuet

Solo with Piano Accompaniment

Ignaz Pleyel (1757-1831)
Austrian Composer
arr. Bruce Pearson and Ryan Nowlin

MASTERING EXCELLENCE

1. After page 10, #35

Basic Preparatory Exercise

Advanced Preparatory Exercise

Mastering Excellence

2. After page 16, #60

Basic Preparatory Exercise

Advanced Preparatory Exercise

Mastering Excellence

3. After page 18, #73

Basic Preparatory Exercise

Advanced Preparatory Exercise

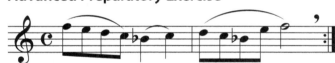

Mastering Excellence

4. After page 22, #79

▶ Use the alternate F♯ fingering on notes with ∗ .

Basic Preparatory Exercise

Advanced Preparatory Exercise

Mastering Excellence

5. After page 24, #93

▶ Use the alternate F♯ fingering on notes with ＊.

Basic Preparatory Exercise

Advanced Preparatory Exercise

Mastering Excellence

6. After page 26, #106

Basic Preparatory Exercise

Advanced Preparatory Exercise

Mastering Excellence

7. After page 30, #129

▶ Use the alternate C fingering on notes with ＊.

Basic Preparatory Exercise

Advanced Preparatory Exercise

Mastering Excellence

Chop Builders

▶ Mix and match exercises 1A, 2A, and 3A in any combination.

1A.

2A.

3A.

1B, 2B, 3B.   ▶ Use this line to accompany 1A, 2A, and 3A.

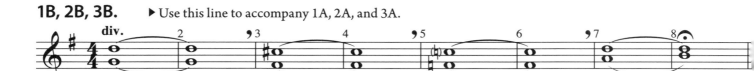

4. Match and Pass That Note

▶ Also play with other articulations:

5. Dynamic Control

G Major Warm-Up (Concert B♭ Major)

1. G Major Scale and Arpeggios

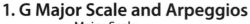

2. G Major Technique Study

▶ Also play with other articulations:

3. G Major Balance and Tuning Study

4. G Major Chorale: All Grace and Thanksgiving

Ryan Nowlin (b. 1978)
American Composer

C Major Warm-Up (Concert E♭ Major)

1. C Major Scale and Arpeggios

2. C Major Technique Study

▶ Also play with other articulations:

3. C Major Balance and Tuning Study

4. C Major Chorale: Make a Joyful Sound

Ryan Nowlin (b. 1978)
American Composer

D Major Warm-Up (Concert F Major)

1. D Major Scale and Arpeggios

2. D Major Technique Study

▶ Also play with other articulations:

3. D Major Balance and Tuning Study

4. D Major Chorale: Celebration and Honor

Ryan Nowlin (b. 1978)
American Composer

SCALE STUDIES

| Theory & Composition | **chromatic scale** – series of 12 ascending or descending half steps |

▶ For notes you do not know, refer to the fingering chart.

1. G Major Scale, Arpeggios, and Thirds (Concert B♭ Major)

2. C Major Scale, Arpeggios, and Thirds (Concert E♭ Major)

3. D Major Scale, Arpeggios, and Thirds (Concert F Major)

4. F Major Scale, Arpeggios, and Thirds (Concert A♭ Major)

5. Chromatic Scale

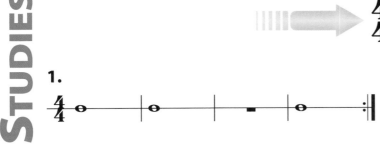

RHYTHM STUDIES

1.

11.

2.

12.

3.

13.

4.

14.

5.

15.

6.

16.

7.

17.

8.

18.

9.

19.

10.

20.

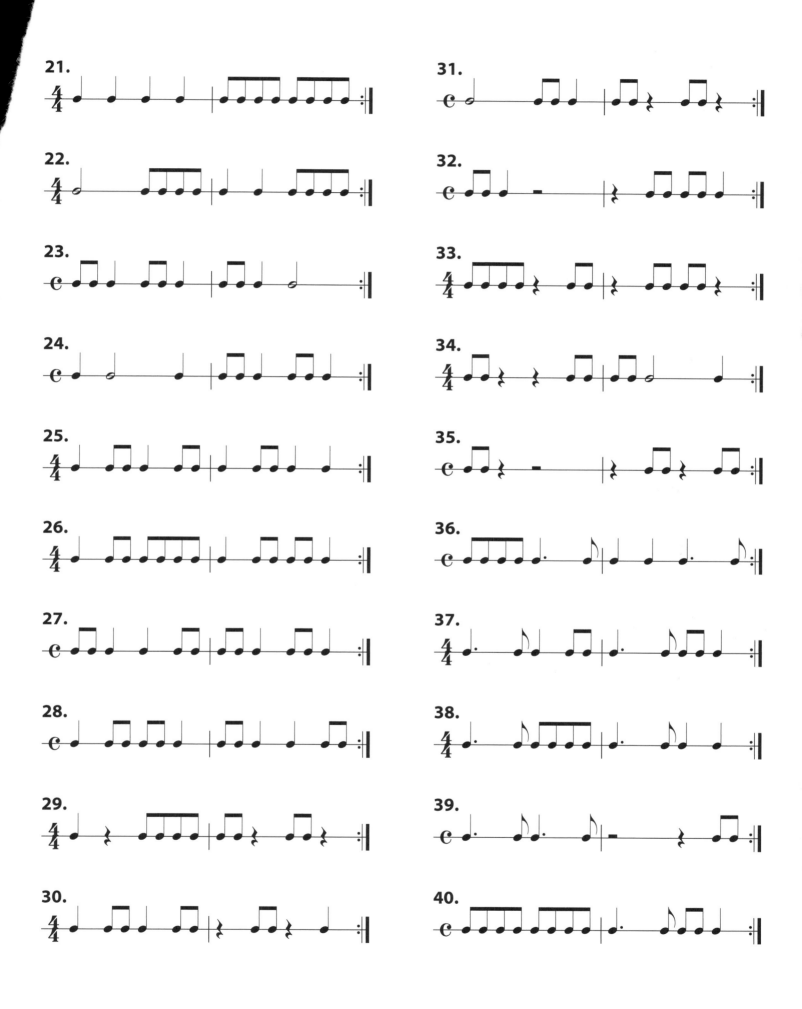

World Map

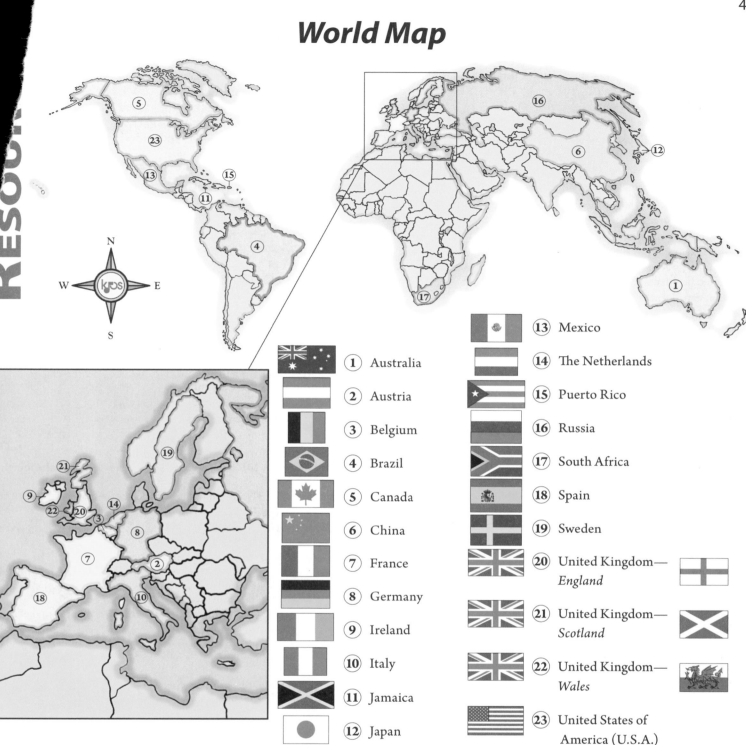

1. Australia
2. Austria
3. Belgium
4. Brazil
5. Canada
6. China
7. France
8. Germany
9. Ireland
10. Italy
11. Jamaica
12. Japan
13. Mexico
14. The Netherlands
15. Puerto Rico
16. Russia
17. South Africa
18. Spain
19. Sweden
20. United Kingdom—*England*
21. United Kingdom—*Scotland*
22. United Kingdom—*Wales*
23. United States of America (U.S.A.)

About the Alto Saxophone

Belgian clarinetist Adolphe Sax invented the saxophone in 1841 and patented his invention in 1846 in Paris. The family of saxophone instruments was invented to bridge the woodwind and brass sections of an orchestra or band. Of the original 14 different saxophones, the E♭ alto saxophone, the B♭ tenor saxophone, and the E♭ baritone saxophone are still in common use today. The B♭ soprano saxophone is also used, mostly in jazz and small ensemble music. The C tenor is still used only in particular orchestral pieces. Each saxophone uses the same fingerings, which allows musicians to alternate among these instruments with ease. The pitch and range of each saxophone is determined by the length of its tubing. The longer tubing in larger instruments allows for lower ranges to be played.

The saxophone's combination of metal body and wooden reed allows it to blend equally well with brass or woodwind instruments. The instrument is classified as a member of the woodwind family because the key system is similar to that of the flute, and because it has a reed.

The alto saxophone is mainly played in modern concert and marching bands, jazz ensembles, small chamber groups, saxophone quartets, as a solo instrument, and occasionally in orchestras.

FUN FACTS

▶ Besides the saxophones and an improved bass clarinet, Adolphe Sax also created a set of keyed bugles called saxhorns, which provided a foundation for the euphonium.

▶ Hector Berlioz was the first well-known composer to use saxophone in symphonic music.

▶ Check out these saxophonists: Eugene Rousseau, Marcel Mule, Sigurd Rascher, Debra Richtmeyer, and Charlie Parker.

Glossary/Index

accent – (p. 18) emphasize the note

accidental – (p. 11) symbol that alters the pitch of a note until the end of the measure

Allegro – (p. 18) fast tempo

anacrusis – (p. 16) see **pick-up**

Andante – (p. 18) walking tempo; slower than **Moderato**

arpeggio – (p. 23) notes of a chord sounded one after another

articulation – (p. 10) type of attack used to play a note or group of notes

bar line – (pp. 4-6) divides the staff into measures

breath mark – (p. 7) take a breath

cautionary accidental – (p. 24) see **courtesy accidental**

chord – (p. 20) two or more notes sounded at the same time

chromatic scale – (p. 43) scale of 12 ascending or descending half steps

closing – (p. 20) last measures of a composition, often containing new material added to give a feeling of finality

common time – (p. 9) means the same as $\frac{4}{4}$

composition – (p. 9) creation of music that can be performed later, usually from written notation

courtesy accidental – (p. 24) reminder that the bar line has canceled an accidental

crescendo – (p. 22) gradually louder

Da Capo al Fine (*D.C. al Fine*) – (p. 26) go back to the beginning of the piece and play or sing until the *Fine*

decrescendo – (p. 22) gradually softer

Divisi (**div.**) – (p. 22) some performers play or sing the top notes while others play or sing the bottom notes

dominant – (p. 20) fifth note of a scale; chord built on the fifth note of a scale

duet – (p. 7) piece of music featuring two different parts played or sung together

dynamics – (p. 17) softness or loudness of a piece of music

embouchure – (p. 3) mouth formation used to play an instrument

fermata – (p. 12) hold a note or rest longer than its usual value

final double bar line – (pp. 4-6) marks the end of the music

1st and 2nd endings – (p. 12) play or sing the 1st ending the first time through, repeat, skip the 1st ending, and play or sing the 2nd ending

flat – (p. 16) lowers the pitch of a note one half step

forte (*f*) – (p. 17) loud

G clef – (pp. 4-6) see **treble clef**

half step – (p. 11) smallest interval used in Western music

harmony – (p. 7) two or more notes played or sung at the same time

improvisation – (p. 15) spontaneous composition of music through playing or singing

interval – (p. 11) distance between two pitches

introduction – (p. 12) opening passage of a piece of music

key signature – (p. 11) sharps or flats placed after a clef

ledger line – (pp. 4-6) short line used for notes above or below the staff

long rest – (p. 20) rest for the number of measures indicated

Maestoso – (p. 27) majestically

major scale – (p. 23) series of whole (w) and half (h) steps in the following pattern: wwhwwwh

measure – (pp. 4-6) area between two bar lines

mezzo forte (*mf*) – (p. 18) medium loud

mezzo piano (*mp*) – (p. 18) medium soft

Moderato – (p. 18) medium tempo

multiple-measure rest – (p. 20) see **long rest**

music alphabet – (pp. 4-6) first seven letters of the alphabet; these n names are assigned to the lines and spaces of the staff

natural – (p. 16) cancels a flat or sharp

one-measure repeat sign – (p. 10) play or sing the previous measure again

orchestration – (p. 23) choice of instruments used to play the music

phrase – (p. 9) musical sentence, often 4 or 8 measures long

piano (*p*) – (p. 17) soft

pick-up – (p. 16) music that comes before the first full measure of a piece

rehearsal number – (p. 12) find important places in the music using these markers

repeat sign – (p. 9) play or sing the music again

ritardando (*ritard.* or *rit.*) – (p. 30) gradually slow the tempo

round – (p. 9) song in which the same part is played or sung by two or more groups starting at different times

sharp – (p. 11) raises the pitch of a note one half step

sight-reading – (p. 7) playing or singing a piece of music for the first time

slur – (p. 10) articulation that connects notes of *different* pitches; indicates a very smooth sound

Soli – (p. 9) a small group or section plays or sings

Solo – (p. 9) only one person plays or sings

staccato – (p. 25) shorten the note

staff – (pp. 4-6) 5 lines and 4 spaces for writing music

subdominant – (p. 20) fourth note of a scale; chord built on the fourth note of a scale

syncopation – (p. 31) rhythmic effect that places emphasis on a weak beat

tempo – (p. 18) speed of a piece of music

ternary form – (p. 34) music with three sections: Section A, followed by a contrasting Section B, then Section A again

theme – (p. 12) a melody within a piece of music

theme and variation – (p. 16) type of composition that begins with a main melody (**theme**) and continues with different versions (**variations**) of the main melody

tie – (p. 11) marking that connects notes of the *same* pitch to make one longer note

time signature – (pp. 4-6) top number tells you the number of counts per measure; bottom number tells you the type of note that gets one count

tonic – (p. 20) first note of a scale; chord built on the first note of a scale

treble clef – (pp. 4-6) the line it circles on the staff is called **G**

trio (ensemble) – (p. 12) piece of music featuring three different parts played or sung together

trio (march) – (p. 34) third theme in a march, typically a contrasting section

Tutti – (p. 9) everyone plays or sings

unisono (**unis.**) – (p. 22) everyone plays or sings the same notes

variation – (p. 16) see **theme and variation**

whole step – (p. 23) interval consisting of two half steps

Timeline

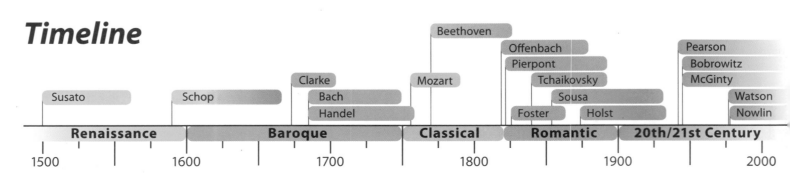